SPOOKY
ACTIVITY BOOK

by Kate Brookes
Illustrated by Martin Ursell

CONTENTS

MICHAEL O'MARA BOOKS LIMITED

You are invited to a grave rave at Castle Disgusto to celebrate Count Dracula's 900th birthday. The horror begins at the stroke of midnight. R.I.P

DRESS Horribly

Count Dracula's invited the cream of the creeps including Frankenstein's monster, a werewolf or two, a coven of witches and wizards, and a spook of ghosts, ghouls, poltergeists and zombies to his birthday. Because of a terrible mix-up at the post office, you have received an invitation. (A colony of vampire bats are now going to your best friend's roller-blading party.)

As you know nothing about mixing with the recently departed, the invisible and the just plain gross, let me help you out. I'll be your right-hand man (sadly that's all I am, just a right hand). I'll show you how to dress and cook in bad taste, how to turn your bedroom into a dreadroom, and how to make the most perfectly horrid present for Count Dracula. And, because I'm the ghost with the most, I'll show you some hair-raising tricks to play on your friends.

Now don't be afraid, come join the party. The spooks will be on their best behaviour, I hope.

DIE LAUGHING

What do polite vampires say?
Fangs very much.

Where does Dracula get all his jokes?
From a crypt writer.

When do ghosts play tricks on each other?
On April Ghoul's Day.

The Haunted House of Horror

Can't think of anything to buy for the Count? Well, how about making a witch's bed-sit complete with leaping skeleton and,. most disgusting of all, a washing line of witch's knickers. Too revolting!

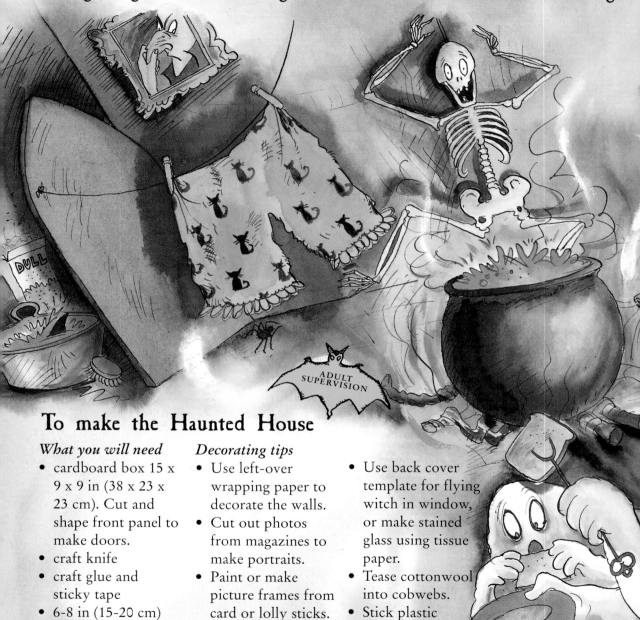

To make the Haunted House

What you will need
- cardboard box 15 x 9 x 9 in (38 x 23 x 23 cm). Cut and shape front panel to make doors.
- craft knife
- craft glue and sticky tape
- 6-8 in (15-20 cm) fine string
- 2 split pins

Decorating tips
- Use left-over wrapping paper to decorate the walls.
- Cut out photos from magazines to make portraits.
- Paint or make picture frames from card or lolly sticks.
- Paint a stone floor and wooden doors.

- Use back cover template for flying witch in window, or make stained glass using tissue paper.
- Tease cottonwool into cobwebs.
- Stick plastic critters in dark corners.

Psst!

Keep doors closed by inserting a split-pin (legs to the inside of the house) alongside the door. Open the legs to catch door.

Witch's washing line

Cut a door from a piece of stiff card and securely tape one edge to a wall. Tape one end of the string to the door, the other to the wall. If string is visible with door closed, shorten the string. Cut out the witch's laundry from wrapping paper and tape to the line.

Leaping skeleton!

1 Draw cauldron and fire with tabs as shown. Glue ends of the tabs to the wall. Draw and cut out skeleton.

2 In wall behind cauldron cut a 6 in (15 cm) slit starting 1 in (3 cm) up from the floor.

3 Push a split pin into skeleton. Pass pin legs through slit and open them slightly. To make skeleton leap slide the pin.

Aaaaargh! that's hot!

5

Dressed to shock

Whether you're dressing to thrill the neighbours or to impress Count Dracula, no self-respecting spook would be seen dead in anything but basic black. This 'Rogue' fashion feature gives you the low-down know-how on dressing and making-up for a night on the howl.

Ms Bee Witched

When playing Ms Bee Witched, you must cackle, mutter curses, spit spells and stick your warty nose where it's not wanted.

How to do the make-up

Using face paint, make your face and neck green (yes, green), and use a black face crayon or eyeliner to outline your lips and draw wrinkles. Colour your eyelids white and your lips dark red.

To make the cloak, hat, long nails and pointed nose see pages 8-9.

Vlad the Cad

Dressing up as a vampire is dead simple. All you need is a cloak, a handful of talons, a mouthful of fangs and a thirst.

How to do the make-up

Cover face and neck with white face paint or talcum powder. Paint your lips blood red. Circle your eyes first in black and then red. Make your eyebrows black and bushy. Slick your hair with gel.

To make the cloak and long nails see pages 8-9.

6

The Severed Finger

Cut the sleeve and drawer of a matchbox as shown. Line the drawer, leaving the hole uncovered, with cotton wool splattered with red paint.

Slip your finger into the hole, replace the sleeve and then scare your friends. Even scarier if you wriggle your 'severed' finger.

Desmodus

To create a truly batifying spectacle be light on your feet, flap your wings and squeak. When it comes to eating, Des likes his meat alive and moving. Yeuk!

How to do the make-up
Paint face, neck, lips and ears black, leaving only flesh-coloured circles around the eyes and on the tip of the nose. Vampire bats also need fangs!
To make the ears, cloak and chalk white claws see pages 8-9.

Frankenstein's Monster

This monster is really BIG so you've got to walk tall and walk ugly. Wear tatty clothes that are far too small and a nasty scowl. Pad out shoulders with folded newspaper and wear your meanest boots.

How to do the make-up
Gel most hair back and whiten your face with face paint. Draw heavy lines and scars in black and red. Paint lips red.
To make neck bolts and veined hands see pages 8-9.

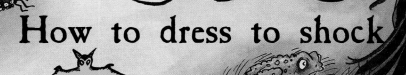

How to dress to shock

Witch's nose

What you will need

- plasticine
- 1 sheet of newspaper torn into 1 in (2.5 cm) squares
- wallpaper paste or water-based glue
- craft knife
- paint
- thin elastic

1

Remember to make nostril holes

Mould nose in plasticine. (Base of the nose should cover your own nose).

2

Make warts with small balls of newspaper

Cover mould with 4 overlapping layers of lightly pasted news-paper. Allow to dry.

When dry, paint the nose and attach elastic

Cut the papier mâché nose in half. Remove plasticine. Join halves with pasted paper.

Batty ears

What you will need

- pink or red card
- black felt-tip pen
- plastic hair band to match hair colour
- stapler and tape

Draw a pair of ears as shown and cut out. Snip along the dotted line, overlap the edges a little and staple. Tape ears facing forward on to the band.

Nails, claws and withered hand

What you will need

- card to match your skin colour
- red or black felt-tip pens
- white paint (for bat claws)
- sticky tape
- make-up: dark eyeliner and eye shadow
- talcum powder

Trace this fake nail and band 10 times on to card. Colour the nails. Position a fake nail on your finger, fit the band around and secure with tape. Repeat for each finger

To make hands look veiny and withered: draw veins with eyeliner pencil, brush dark eye shadow between knuckles, and sprinkle hands with talcum powder.

For vampire nails and bat claws follow the dotted line and cut out.

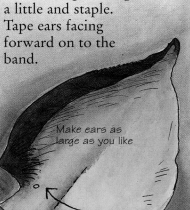

Make ears as large as you like

Cloak

What you will need

- large black bin-liner
- scissors
- sticky tape
- 1 yard (1m) black ribbon (red for vampire cloak)
- stapler
- stiff red card (for vampire cloak)

Vampire's collar

Sticky tape

Ribbon

Staples

Collar is same width as the gathered neck of the cloak

1. Cut open bin-liner into a rectangle and make a 2 in (4 cm) hem. Secure with tape.

2. Thread ribbon through hem and gather the cloak. Fix gathers by stapling ribbon.

3. To make vampire's collar: cut red card as shown. Tape collar to cloak.

Monster's neck bolt!

What you will need

- 15 x 1 in (38 x 2.5 cm) band of skin-coloured card
- black felt-tip pen
- wine cork, cut in half
- corrugated board
- aluminium foil
- PVA glue
- sticky tape

1. Draw fake scar and stitches on band. Cut 2 circular discs from corrugated board.

2. Glue a cork to centre of each disc. Cover all in foil except end of cork.

3. Place band round your neck. Position bare cork ends and glue onto band. When ready, tape ends of band together.

Discs to be slightly larger than diameter of cork

Witch's hat

What you will need

- sheet of newspaper
- 2 sheets of black card
- sticky tape and glue
- long, thin strips of crêpe paper for hair

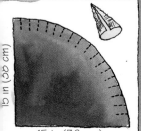

15 in (38 cm)

15 in (38 cm)

2

3

Hole in each ring is same size as the base of the cone above the flaps

4

Decorate hat with a spider

Cut newspaper as shown to form a cone. Adjust for size, trace on to black card.

Cut out hat and snip card following dotted lines. Form cone and secure with tape.

Cut 2 rings. Open out flaps on the cone, and glue one ring to the upper side of flaps.

Glue crêpe hair to the underside of flaps. Glue remaining ring to bottom of hat.

Castle Disgusto

How to turn your bedroom into a dreadroom. Beware! Your room will look so much like Castle Disgusto that werewolves and other unwelcome guests will want to move in! (Parents, on the other hand, won't come anywhere near.)

To scare your friends or family secretly make a tape recording of screams, howls, rattling chains, footsteps and hooting owls. Don't record all the sounds one after another – leave a couple of minutes between each one. Make some loud and others quiet. Hide your tape player so you can switch it on unnoticed.

Here lies SAM who was always playing tricks.

Screech

How many Eeeek! Eyeba can you spot in this illustration?
Answer on page 16

Hovering Horrors

Skulking Spiders

What you will need

- cardboard tube
- 5 pipe-cleaners
- black, red, yellow poster paints and brush
- thin elastic or white thread
- sticky tape
- yellow paper for the eyes

1 Cut tube to 2 in (5 cm) long. Paint black. When dry, make 2 holes for fangs.

2 Bend a small piece of pipe cleaner to make fangs, push through holes. Paint fangs red.

3 Paint red and yellow stripes on pipe-cleaners. Paint or stick on eyes.

Attach line and hang up.

Wind sticky tape round the middle of four pipe-cleaners. Fix to inside of tube.

Flying Ghosts

What you will need

- white balloon
- lightweight white bin-liner
- white thread
- black paper for eyes and mouth
- glue
- nylon fishing line

How to make your ghost fly

Hide your ghost in a wardrobe, run the free end of the line over the hanging rail and tape it to the top outer edge of the opened wardrobe door. When you close the door, the ghost will drop to the bottom, but when the door is opened, it will fly to the top.

1 Half inflate the balloon and knot the end. Turn the bin-liner inside out and put balloon inside.

2 Gather bin-liner together and tie with fishing line. Glue on eyes and mouth.

Never put plastic bags over your head

Tape a long piece of fishing line to top of ghost.

Eeeek! Eyeballs

What you will need

- table tennis balls
- coloured paper
- large sewing needle
- glue
- felt-tip pens
- thin elastic

Cut pupil and iris from the coloured paper. Glue to the ball. Draw red wiggly lines all around the eyeball. **Yeuk!**

Thread a large sewing needle with elastic and push it through the ball from bottom to top. Knot the bottom end and hang up.

ADULT SUPERVISION

Are you Game?

The ghosts and ghouls are restless. They're getting up to mischief, so entertain them with these ghastly games from beyond the grave.

Pass the coffin

You will need
- a coffin-shaped box containing a prize
- 1 or 2 small prizes per guest
- lots of paper to wrap the package
- slips of paper and pen for noting forfeits
- music

Simply a spooky version of 'Pass the Parcel' but with forfeits. Prepare the parcel as you would for Pass the Parcel, but put a prize and a forfeit on a paper slip in every layer. When the music stops and a guest unwraps a layer of paper, they will be asked to do a forfeit (see Forfeit Ideas) before they can claim their suitably horrible prize.

What's in the Witch's larder?

The perfect way to whet (or ruin) your guests' appetites is to play this game. Conceal inside separate bags or containers items which feel like body parts. For example: a damp sponge for a tongue, peeled grapes for eyeballs, dried apricots for ears, cold spaghetti for entrails, cauliflower for a brain, peeled peach for a heart, twigs and sticks for bones. The bags are passed around for everyone to feel and to guess what's inside. Warning: not a game for the squeamish!

Trick or treat

Fill a clear container with large red peeled grapes and diluted blackcurrant cordial. Label the container 'Fresh eyeballs'. Guests who lose a game or refuse to do a forfeit must eat one of the eyeballs.

Forfeit ideas:
tell a monstrously awful joke, make a seriously ugly face, reveal a deep dark secret about yourself, find words that rhyme with 'ghost' and 'ghoul', or sing a spooky song.

Ghost–busters

You will need
- 1 white balloon for each guest
- string

Inflate the balloons. Tie one to the ankle of each guest. The aim of the game is to burst the balloons of the others by stamping on them. Ghost-busting continues until there is only one person left with an inflated balloon.

Living dead

You will need
- white sheet
- cushion

Everyone apart from the host and one guest leave the room. The host lies on the floor, the cushion is placed over his feet and he is covered by the sheet. Place his shoes at top of his head. One guest at a time is invited in to pay respects to the dead. When he kneels beside the supposed corpse's head and bows, the corpse comes to life and surprises him with a whack on the back.

Witch's night out

You will need
- bar of chocolate
- knife, fork and a plastic plate
- 1 dice
- witch's hat, plastic fingernails or oversized gloves, and a cloak

Everyone sits in a circle round the witch's outfit, knife, fork and plate of unwrapped chocolate. Each in turn tries to throw a 6 with a dice. The first to do so dons the outfit and tries to cut off a chocolate square using the knife and fork. At the same time the others try and throw a 6. As soon as someone does so, they take over the role of the witch. A fast game that quickly gets out of hand.

Who's the most important member of a ghost football team?
The ghoulie, naturally.
What games do skeletons play in cemeteries?
Corpse and robbers.
What did the young bear want for his birthday?
A deadly bear!

ADULT SUPERVISION

Nasty Nibbles

The Count loves bad taste party food that's still moving, which is why it's called Cauldron Bleu cooking. Eat up! Enjoy! This could be someone's last meal...

Skull pizzas

To make 6 pizzas
- 6 cheese slices
- 6 individual-sized pizza bases
- tomato paste
- 12 slices pepperoni
- 3 button mushrooms, halved
- 1 red pepper, diced

1 Cut cheese slices to resemble skulls.

2 Spread tomato paste on the pizza bases and top with the cheese skulls.

3 Use pepperoni for eyes, half a mushroom for a nose cavity (gross eh!) and pepper slices for the teeth.

4 Cook according to instructions on the pizza base wrapping.

The Cauldron Bleu
Mean-you

Spaghetti brain-onaise
Cocktail sausage fingers served
with Tom's-toe sauce
Mashed potato slime
Mouldy leftovers
Legs mayonose
Beingburgers
Ghoulash
Rack of pain
Stewed newt
Jellied heels
Fried lice

Jellied Right-Hand Man

To make 1 hand

- 1 new right-handed rubber glove, thoroughly washed
- 2 pkts lime jelly
- red food colouring
- 2 red and 2 black licorice laces
- clothes pegs or similar

1 Dissolve jelly in 1/2 pint (300 ml) boiling water. When dissolved, add 1/2 pint (300 ml) cold water.

2 Pour jelly into glove. To seal the opening, fold it over twice and clamp with pegs.

3 Lie glove palm-down on a flat plate. Make sure fingers are spaced. Freeze overnight until well set.

4 Remove glove by cutting down the length of it and each finger. Glove will peel off easily.

5 Colour nails and severed wrist with red food colouring. Use licorice to make veins. Serve with 'I scream'.

15

Creepy-crawly spiders

To make 6 crawlies
- 6 chocolate-covered marshmallow cakes
- 12 thin licorice laces
- 6 glacé cherries, halved
- 1 tbs icing sugar mixed with a little water

1 Cut each licorice lace into 4 for legs (8 per spider).
2 Make small holes in cake and insert licorice.
3 For eyes: cherry halves stuck on with a dab of icing. Refrigerate.

Puffed-up nasties

To make 20 shapes
- flour
- ready-made puff pastry
- 2 oz (50 g) grated cheese
- beaten egg

1 On a floured surface roll out pastry until 1/8th in (3 mm) thick.
2 Sprinkle cheese on one half and fold over the remaining pastry to make a cheese sandwich.
3 Roll the pastry flat and, with a knife, cut out nasties: fangs, snakes, coffins, broom-sticks and bats.
4 Place on greased trays, brush with egg and bake in oven for 10 minutes at 220° C / 425°F or Gas Mark 7.

Vampire's thirst-quencher

To make 12 glasses
- 1 pint (600 ml) diluted black-currant cordial
- 1 pint (600 ml) orange juice
- 1 pint (600 ml) lemonade
- 1-2 pkts strawberry jelly cubes, cut into small pieces
- peeled grapes (eyeballs!)
- plastic snakes, spiders, witch's fingers.

Put all the ingredients into a large punch bowl and serve at room temperature. (Vampires like their refreshments warm!) To boost colour add a couple of drops of red food dye (optional).

Let your friends serve themselves and watch them squirm at the bobbing eyeballs, wildlife and slime.

Slurp! slurp!